THE ROPE OF LOVE

THE
ROPE OF LOVE

Around the Earth in Song

WRITTEN
COMPOSED AND ARRANGED BY
DONALD SWANN

WITH DRAWINGS BY
SISTER MEINRAD CRAIGHEAD

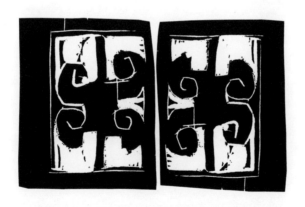

THE BODLEY HEAD
LONDON SYDNEY
TORONTO

Acknowledgments

The publishers have made every effort to trace the ownership of the copyright material in this book. It is their belief that the necessary permissions from publishers, authors and authorised agents have been obtained, but in the event of any question arising as to the use of any material, the publishers, while expressing regrct for any error unconsciously made, will be pleased to make the necessary corrections in future editions of this book.

Thanks are due to the following for permission to reprint copyright material. Chappell & Company (London and Sydney) for *Carol of the Birds*; Schwann Verlag for Peter Janssens' *Eia Susani*; DPS Publicity Limited for permission to use David Goodall's *I Want to go Out*; Caryl Micklem for the words and music of *Don't Wait for an Angel*; Essex Music Ltd for the words and music of *Half the World*; The Missionaries of Charity (Co-Workers of Mother Teresa) for the use of Mother Teresa's daily prayer, *Make us Worthy, Lord*.

All the other material is reprinted by permission of Galliard Ltd, 82 High Road, East Finchley, London N2 9PW.

Contents

All choral and piano arrangements are by Donald Swann

DIAGRAMS for GUITAR CHORDS

[x = string not played]   [o = play open string]

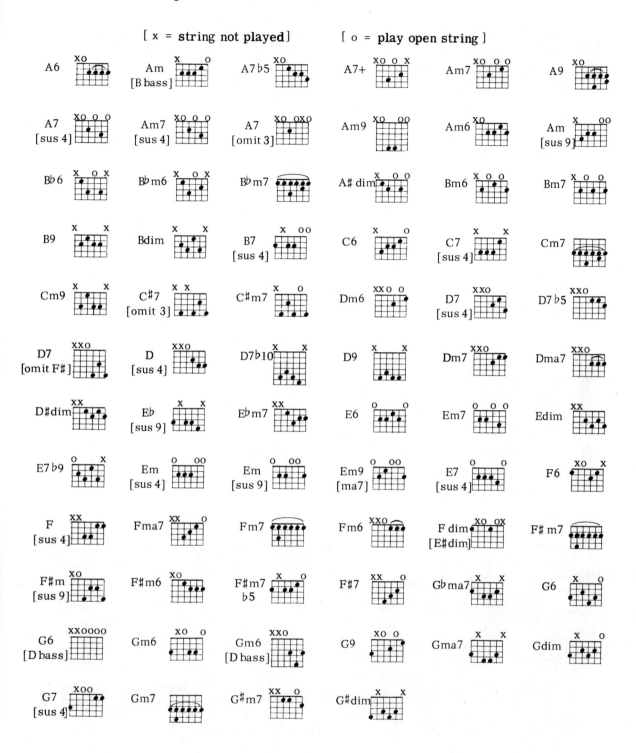

These six chords may be transposed up to give any major, minor or 7th

F   Fm   F7   Bb   Bbm   Bb7

BLESSED are the merciful
ESSED are the HUNGRY
ARE THE PEACEMAKERS
BLESSED ARE THE POOR
SED are the GENTLE

Foreword

This is an anthology of contemporary carols that I have written, arranged or adapted over a period of five years. In *Sing Round the Year*, my previous anthology, I attempted to define the term carol as broadly as possible and I examined the matter of why carols are not only Christmas carols. I hope that controversy is now over. I offer these twenty carols to speak for me; each one has redefined the carol for me in yet a new way.

For *Sing Round the Year* I selected carols for all seasons, and in many different styles; this time there is a new dimension—a geographical one. I have borrowed from Germany, Greece, Cyprus, Russia, Vietnam, Australia, British Honduras, West Indies and Northern Arizona. However in no case have I picked up foreign words or music just for the variety, as in a stamp collector's mixed envelope. Each song has arisen naturally and become by adaptation or composition a part of my repertoire. I nearly used as my sub-title 'Twenty carols internalised by Donald Swann' but decided it would sound as though I'd swallowed them!

To introduce each piece I have provided a paragraph or two of comment. These comments are based on the introductions I normally give my songs in performance. Perhaps it isn't necessary to 'talk-in' songs to audiences but my friend Michael Flanders did so in the *At the Drop of a Hat* shows and I picked up the habit from him. In this instance I hope also that the words will give a unity of idea to the whole book.

In some of the comments the reader will find hints for musicians but here is the general guide. The accompaniments are for the piano; organists are welcome to adapt them to their use. Guitar symbols have been added nearly everywhere, plus a page of 'harder chords' explained by the excellent guitarist and teacher, George Adie. Occasional percussion instruments are suggested and there is one item where the trumpet can play a vital (though not obligatory) part. Vocal arrangements vary from one to two, and rarely to four, voices, but every carol would survive on one voice only.

I love variety but do not wish the search for it in this book to make the result too hard for the average performer. The overall rule is, if anything is too hard, draw a deep breath, count like mad and come up smiling a few bars later.

May I say a word about the illustrations for this book? Sydney Carter, that intrepid explorer of new ideas, and I, had fallen under the influence of Sister Corita Kent's colourful serigraphs which overflow on the walls of the *avant-garde* churches in New York and reminded both of us that the revaluations in faith we both sought from new words and music could appear on walls as well as on paper. One day in London, Sydney spotted Sister Meinrad's woodcut-word-prints in Heals. He telephoned at once, 'You've got to go and see them'. I went to see them and was thrilled.

When this book was growing I was on a short holiday in Hereford and completed it by telephoning the enclosed Benedictine Monastery of Stanbrook Abbey and asking, somewhat timorously, if I could be introduced to Sister Meinrad, the artist. 'Parlour at 10.30,' a cheerful voice told me, 'and a room booked for you in the hostel.' I met not only Sister Meinrad but Sister Hildelith, who prints exquisite books, and Sister Miriam, who sang several of Sydney's carols while I accompanied her on the piano that stood on the 'secular' side of the long table. Finally, the Abbess entered and gave her approval to this scene. At this point I realised that Sister Meinrad and her colleagues were closer to 'the Land that is Immortal' than I shall ever be, but were mortal enough to enjoy an earthly carol as much as the beautiful plainsong they sing daily. I left the manuscript of this carol book, knowing I'd reached home.

Sister Meinrad is an American and has won widespread recognition in her own country as a printmaker before entering Stanbrook. I am delighted that she undertook to work on this book. I've asked her permission to reproduce a drawing she sent me in a letter for the opening night of my show *Between the Bars*.

DONALD SWANN

I
God's Riddle

This first carol is by Malcolm Stewart who was once a Roman Catholic priest, but who left this vocation to be a writer. He then became a television executive, then explored Buddhism with a guitar in Ceylon. I first heard his songs when he produced a short record called *Let's Play a Game*, and I became fascinated by his approach to faith as a quest or a playful searching. One day he appeared with a new song in this vein, *God's Riddle*. It had his words and tune but I took to it so strongly that I made an arrangement for piano there and then. 'God has set us a riddle,' says Malcolm. 'He is here, he is near, turn around and you might see or hear him—a bit like playing grandmother's footsteps. Look at David, God was close to him when he danced and close to him when he wept.' At the time when I heard this song, my own mind was clogged by different ideas on faith, all of which I found hard to compare and to assimilate, so this lightness of touch in Malcolm's song appealed to me greatly.

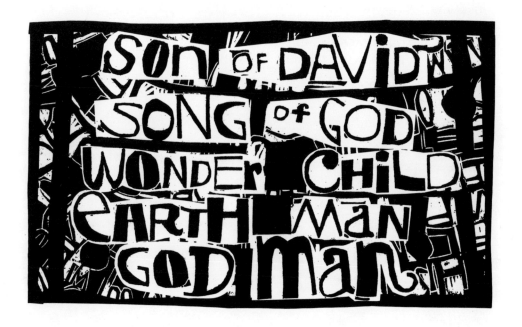

God's Riddle

I was in David who danced in Jerusalem.
I was in David lamenting for Absalom.
I have sung a thousand times
In men forgotten but whose lives were diamond.
Many watched my birth, then I died,
But I left them still
With mirth among them
For the song I sang them.

Can you tell my name
Or say from where I came?
I'm born and dead and living just the same.

I am in sorrow and I am in laughter.
I was here before you and I'm following after.
Sadly I am dying, then I'm gladly rising
All the earth surprising.
Some have searched the silent skies
And blamed me for a million lies,
They are so near me
That they just don't hear me.

I am where you stand.
You are who I am.
I'm the word of God, I live in man.

God's Riddle

Words and Music by
MALCOLM STEWART

Easy, smooth tempo ♩ = 66

cant.

mp

con pedale

I was in Da-vid who danced in Je-ru-sa-lem. I was in Da-vid la-

men-ting for Ab-sa-lom. I have sung a thou-sand times In men for-got-ten but whose

lives were dia-mond. Ma-ny watched my birth, then I died, But I left them still With mirth a - mong them For the song I sang them. Can you tell my name Or say from where I came? I'm

born and dead and li-ving just the same.

AUDIENCE or CHOIR *reprise*

Can you tell my name Or say from where I came? I'm

born and dead and li-ving just the same.

I am in sor-row and I am in laugh-ter. I was

here be - fore you and I'm fol - low - ing af -ter. Sad -ly I am dy-ing, then I'm

glad -ly ri -sing All the earth sur - pri-sing.

Some have searched the si -lent skies And blamed me for a mil -lion lies, They

are so near me That they just don't hear me.

Dm7   **G7**   **Cm7**   **F7**

I am where you stand.   You are who I am.

C   **A7**   **D7**   **G7**   **C**

I'm the word of God, I live in man.

AUDIENCE or CHOIR *reprise*

Dm7   **G7**   **Cm7**   **F7**

I am where you stand.   You are who I am.

pochiss. più mosso

C   **A7**   **D7**   **G7**   **C**   **B♭6**   **G7**   **C**

I'm the word of God, I live in man.

poco rit.

2

Carol of the Birds

I once spent a few months in Australia. It is quite a long time ago now, and I yearn to go there again. The landscape, the unfamiliar vegetation, the animals and birds (there were opossums outside the Melbourne Hotel—are they still there?) and the character of the people fascinated me; and though it is a simple delight I was charmed to eat Christmas dinner in a temperature of 101 degrees. I soon learned that the Australians get weary of reindeer carols, with Father Christmas jingling through the snow, and some years ago John Wheeler and William James made a contribution to counteract the situation, with a collection of new Australian 'warm' carols. One of them especially took my fancy, the *Carol of the Birds*, and my children and I learned it together. Here are the plants—the tree-ferns and the wattles; and the birds—the brolgas, bell-birds and currawongs. Here also is the warmth but the tune is very bright and clear. A few Australians I have met since my visit seem shy about these indigenous carols, are as hesitant about ramming lorikeets down our throats as I am about dosing them with one more wassail bowl—Michael Flanders' Figgy Duff Carol (No. 10) is an exception, of course! I say it is a fair exchange—and thank them for the lovely aboriginal word in the last line of each verse 'Orana' which means 'welcome'.

Carol of the Birds

Out on the plains the Brolgas are dancing,
Lifting their feet like war-horses prancing:
Up to the sun the woodlarks go winging,
Faint in the dawn light echoes their singing
Orana! Orana! Orana to Christmas Day.

Down where the tree-ferns grow by the river,
There where the waters sparkle and quiver,
Deep in the gullies Bell-birds are chiming,
Softly and sweetly their lyric notes rhyming—
Orana! Orana! Orana to Christmas Day.

Friar birds sip the nectar of flowers,
Currawongs chant in wattle-tree bowers;
In the blue ranges Lorikeets calling—
Carols of bushbirds rising and falling—
Orana! Orana! Orana to Christmas Day.

Carol of the Birds

Words by JOHN WHEELER

Music by WILLIAM G. JAMES

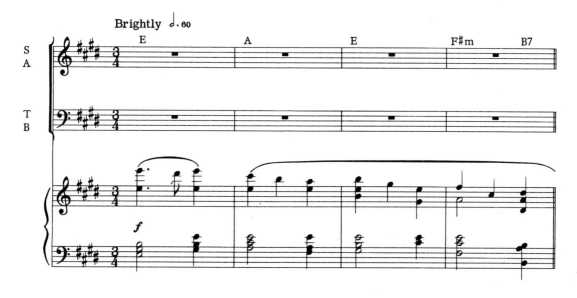

Out on the plains the Brol - gas are dan - cing, Lif - ting their
Down where the tree - ferns grow by the ri - ver, There where the
Fri - ar birds sip the nec - tar of flow - ers, Cur - ra - wongs

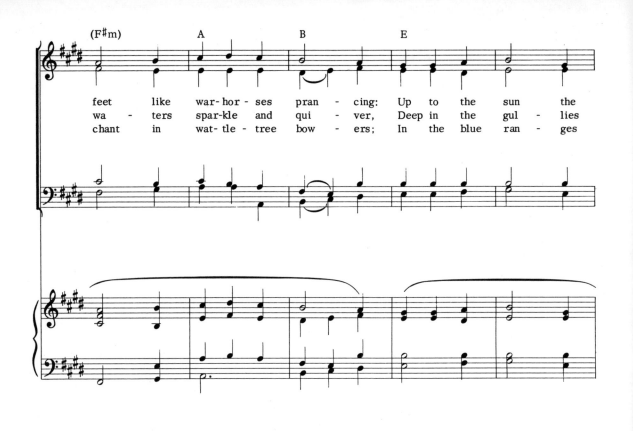

feet like war-hor - ses pran - cing: Up to the sun the
wa - ters spar-kle and qui - ver, Deep in the gul - lies
chant in wat- tle - tree bow - ers; In the blue ran - ges

wood-larks go wing - ing, Faint in the dawn light e - choes their
Bell - birds are chi - ming, Soft - ly and sweet-ly their ly - ric notes
Lor- i - keets cal - ling, Ca - rols of bush - birds ri - sing and

sing-ing O - ra - na! O - ra - na! O - ra - na to Christ - mas
rhy- ming– O - ra - na! O - ra - na! O - ra - na to Christ - mas
fal - ling– O - ra - na! O - ra - na! O - ra - na to Christ - mas

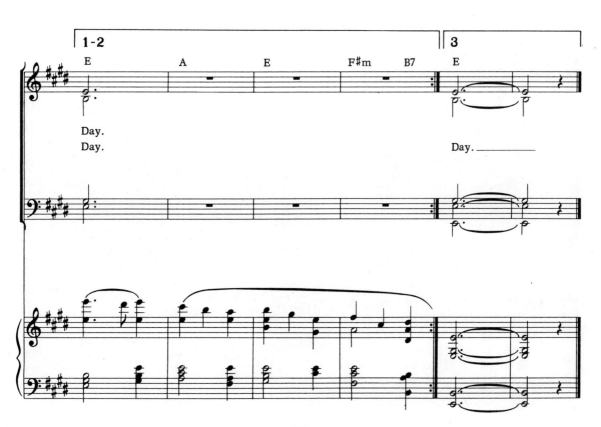

Day.
Day.
Day.

23

THE FRUIT OF THE SPIRIT IS LOVE AND JOY AND PEACE IT IS PATIENCE AND KINDNESS GOODNESS AND TRUSTFULNESS IT IS GENTLENESS AND SELF CONTROL

3

The Air that is Immortal

I first heard the tune of this song in Greece in 1945 and it was one of some fifty I noted down during the three years I lived among the Greek people. The words to that original tune I heard so long ago begin Σεῖς χαρούμενα πουλάκια and are uttered by a Cretan whose country is occupied. 'You birds that fly overhead fly to my fair homeland Greece, and tell them to await me.' A truly magnificent poetic image which has haunted me, as has the tune, for twenty-seven years.

One morning in November 1970 I was in a jumbo jet flying to New York with Sydney Carter. We were on our way to do a lecture called 'Explorations One' in the New World, and we both felt released and excited. The ability to walk freely about a big plane somehow added to our sense of liberation, our imaginations were off the ground. During the journey Sydney wrote a song of his own and I wrote new words to this Greek tune, retaining the one central idea. 'My fair homeland Greece' became in my mind 'My fair homeland Heaven', the immortal land whose freedom we crave, whose clear air we wish to breathe and whose music we long to hear in full, but of which we only hear the echo.

The Air that is Immortal

There's a land that is immortal
But to which I cannot fly.
I can only hear the echo
Of a song beyond the sky.

To the earth my feet are fastened
While you birds fly overhead,
Fly and tell them to await me,
I can hear the dancers' tread.

Here my mind is in confusion,
In a cloud of uncertainty and fear.
Take me to the land of freedom
Where the mind is bright and clear.

I shall go towards the echo
Till I hear that glorious song,
Breathe the air that is immortal
In the land where I belong.

The Air that is Immortal

Words by DONALD SWANN

Music: GREEK TRADITIONAL
adapted by Donald Swann

There's a land that is im-mor-tal But to which I can-not fly. I can on-ly hear the e - cho Of a song be-yond the sky. I can on-ly hear the e - cho Of a song be-yond the sky.

ALL

To the earth my feet are fas - tened While you birds fly o - ver-head,

Fly and tell them to a - wait_____ me, I can hear the dan-cers' tread._____

28

Fly and tell them to a-wait_____ me, I can hear the dan-cers'

tread.

Allegro ♩ = 138

TAMBOURINE

GUITAR E♭ [same rhythm as Tamb.]

mf *cresc.*

E♭m7

Here my mind is in con-fu - sion, In a

cloud of un-cer-tain-ty and fear. Take me to the land of

free - dom Where the mind is bright and clear.

Take me to the land of free - dom Where the mind is bright and clear.

TRUMPET

Allegro ♩ = 138

TAMB.
GUITAR   B♭m   B♭m7   G♭ma7

Moderato ♩ = 120

ff I shall go to-wards the

e - cho Till I hear that glo - rious song,

* *easier alternative*

32

Breathe the air that is im - mor - tal In the land where I be -

8⁻ - - - - - - - - - - - - - - - -

descant

long.   Breathe   the   air   that is   im -

mor - tal   In   the   land   where I   be - long.

rit.

33

Breathe the air that is im - mor - tal In the land where I be - long.

34

Notes on performing *The Air that is Immortal*

Secure a trumpeter, or better still more than one! The trumpet part of course can be played on the organ, as can the whole piece, but a live trumpet is very effective and my first idea.

A tambourine is a great help to the dance $\frac{7}{8}$–$\frac{4}{4}$ sections to give the 'folk dance' feel. In these sections alone, I have added guitar symbols, elsewhere the piece is too flowing for the guitar.

If you can rise to it, costume the trumpeter. I had imagined the trumpeter (from the immortal land) to be dressed to 'radiate glory' in a cross between the Sienese Palio, the annual horse-race in Siena when they wear wonderful mediaeval costumes—the glory of history; the King's Road, Chelsea or Greenwich Village, representing the exuberant colours of this world's youth; and the King in C. S. Lewis's paradisal planet, Perelandra—the majesty of the land immortal or ahead.

Put the trumpeter in a place where he can see the pianist or conductor but out of sight until the end, when he emerges to play the solo passage. The idea behind this lies in the lyric; we are seeking the 'song beyond the sky' but only find it at the end.

In the 'dance' sections, the choir can clap or stamp in rhythm. The more ambitious production could introduce dancers here; I suggest round-dancing to suit Greek tempo. The dancers can act as heralds to the trumpeter; when he emerges they then act as acolytes.

We performed it with all these production effects at Burlington School in Shepherds Bush and it took nearly a term to rehearse the three-and-a-half minute song. But let me end with this . . . if you have only voices and piano, don't worry. Just omit all the interlude sections and sing it straight, going from verse to verse and with no trumpet coda. After all, when I first heard the song it was an unaccompanied Greek melody and the impression has lingered in my mind for twenty-seven years!

4

Eia Susani*

One day I made the acquaintance of Peter Janssens of Münster in Germany. Peter is a composer who has leapt every denominational barrier in Germany. As a Catholic he has made settings of Protestant texts, as in this instance where the words of the original German are by Christine Heuser. He has thousands of young people singing his new style masses on football fields, and he has had bishops disapproving of his church music because there was a drum in it and then cordially approving when the drum was taken out. In fact he has had his difficulties and come out the other side with a whole collection of fine new songs. Peter showed me a number of his Christmas carols and we gave this carol a first English performance on a late night television programme. I was at the piano, Peter played the guitar and we both sang in German. Now I have worked out a translation.

There is a feeling in this song that 'Stille Nacht' is having a well-earned pause, and instead here is the chill air of the *Autobahn* at Christmas-time, modern Germany looking well into the future without fear, and with reverence for Jesus the creator, as well as for Jesus the baby.

* Pronounced Aye-a Soúsani—German for Rock-a-bye Baby.

Eia Susani

Not with these hands, sweet child,
That hold the steering wheel, and handle money,
Can I rock your cradle.
Eia susani, eia susani!
Not with these hands, sweet child,
That are so often hurtful, so destructive,
Can I rock your cradle.
Eia susani, eia susani!

You gave us these hands to touch and to feel,
Have mercy, have mercy on us!
You wish us to hold the steering wheel,
Have mercy, have mercy on us!
Into these hands you gave yourself,
Have mercy, have mercy on us!
And they destroyed you, and they hurt you,
Have mercy, have mercy on us!

Yes, with these hands, sweet child,
To which you gave your blessing, and loved so dearly,
I shall rock your cradle.
Eia susani, eia susani!

Eia Susani

Words by CHRISTINE HEUSER
translated by Donald Swann

Music by PETER JANSSENS

Gently ♩ = 60

Not

with these hands, sweet child, ____ That hold the steer-ing wheel,
with these hands, sweet child, ____ That are so of-ten hurt-ful,

and han-dle mo-ney, Can I rock_ your cra-dle.
__ so de-struc-tive, Can I rock_ your cra-dle.

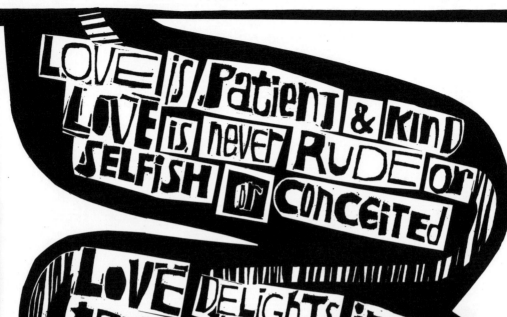

LOVE is patient & kind
LOVE is never RUDE or
SELFISH or CONCEITED

LOVE DELIGHTS in
tRUTH & ENDURES
WHatever COMES

THERE is no Limit to its
FAITH or its HOPE

LOVE WILL NEVER
COME TO AN END

5

The Rope of Love

The Twenty-third Psalm in the Hopi Bible

In the deserts of North Arizona live the Hopi Indians, a poor people whose culture is among the most interesting in North America. Their way of life is called Hopi-Navoti, enshrining a philosophy in which nature and God are one. They are known as a people of peace and sometimes as the Quakers of the desert. The translator of the Twenty-third Psalm in the Hopi Bible has borne in mind that the Hopis are a shepherd people and that David was a shepherd author. So in the psalm God becomes the Shepherd Chief and Heaven the Big Tepee. I love this era of new translations. I saw another Twenty-third Psalm the other day containing this verse: 'Though I am in hospital, and am expected to die, I shall not feel fear, for his injection and his pill will keep me going.' It made me smile, but when I get to that position I shall remember those words.

For a long time I felt my setting of American Indian words to a piano accompaniment was perhaps a strange mixture until I played it in Washington Cathedral. There an American Indian girl came up to me afterwards and said, 'Thanks for using our Rope of Love.' (Confession: there is a Russian folk melody allusion in this, which I use fully in *Christmas Candle*.)

The Rope of Love
The Twenty-third Psalm in the Hopi Bible

The Great Father above a shepherd is. I am his.
He throws out to me a rope, and the name of the rope is love,
And he draws me where the grass is green and the water not
    dangerous
And I eat and I lie down, but he lifts me up again
And draws me to a good road. His name is Wonderful.
Sometimes, it may be very soon, it may be a long time,
He draws me into a valley.
It is dark there, but I will not draw back. I will not be afraid.
For it is between these mountains that the Shepherd Chief will
    meet me,
And the hunger that I have in my heart all through my life will
    be satisfied.
Sometimes he makes the love rope into a whip,
But afterwards he gives me a staff to lean upon.
He spreads a table before me with all kinds of food,
He puts his hand upon my head and the tiredness is gone.
My cup he fills, it runs over. What I tell is true, I lie not.
These roads away ahead will stay with me through this life
    and after,
And afterwards I will go to live in the Big Tepee
And sit down with the Shepherd Chief for ever.

The Rope of Love

Words TRADITIONAL

Music by DONALD SWANN

Lyrics (vocal line):

The Great Fa-ther a-bove a shep-herd is.

I__ am his. He throws out to me a rope, and the

name of the rope is love, And he draws me where the grass is green and the

wa-ter not dan-ge-rous And I eat and I lie down, but he

lifts me up a - gain And draws me to a good road, and

draws me to a good road.

His name is Won-der-ful. Some-times, it may be ve-ry soon, it may be a long time, He draws me in-to a val-ley. It is dark there,— but I will not draw back.— I will not be a- fraid.— For it is be-tween these moun-tains that the Shep-herd Chief will

49

meet me, And the hun-ger that I have in my heart

all through my life will be sa-tis - fied. Some-times he makes the

love rope in-to a whip, But af-ter-wards_ he gives me a staff to lean u-pon. He

spreads a ta-ble be-fore me with all kinds of food, He puts his hand u-pon my

head and the tired-ness is gone. My cup he fills, it runs o-ver. What I

tell is true, I lie_____ not. These roads a-way a - head will

stay with me through this life and af - - - ter, And

af - ter-wards I will go to live in the Big Te - pee And sit down with the

Shep-herd Chief for e - - ver:

And af - ter-wards I will

go to live in the Big Te - pee And sit down with the Shep-herd Chief for

e - - -ver, And sit down with the Shep-herd Chief for e - - ver.

6

West Indian Lord's Prayer

The West Indian, or Caribbean, setting of the Lord's Prayer has gradually entered English Church Music, and has begun to cheer us up with its calypso beat and its restressing of the well-known words, not to mention its chorus 'Hallowed be thy name'. In my church concert *Soundings by Swann* I needed an item to show how instruments other than the organ have gained popularity in new patterns of worship and this version of the Lord's Prayer proved ideal. I have often seen it in religious folk song books but never yet with a complete accompaniment. I hope that I have provided it here, a simple piano part with one variation, the cross-rhythms notated for percussion— we used maraccas, tambourines and claves—and the guitar chords. Double-bass can be readily added, and of course yet other instruments *ad lib*.

I have never been to the West Indies so I have assimilated this song from the strong West Indian British tradition, and I thank the West Indians for it along with more cheerful cricket and a better Health Service, not to mention the buses!

West Indian Lord's Prayer

Our Father who art in Heaven,
Hallowed be Thy Name.
Thy Kingdom come, Thy Will be done,
Hallowed by Thy Name.
On the earth as it is in Heaven,
Hallowed be Thy Name.
Give us this day our daily bread,
Hallowed be Thy Name.
Forgive us all our trespasses,
Hallowed be Thy Name.
As we forgive those who trespass against us,
Hallowed be Thy Name.
And lead us not into temptation,
Hallowed be Thy Name.
But deliver us from all that is evil,
Hallowed be Thy Name.
For Thine is the Kingdom, the Power, and the Glory,
Hallowed be Thy Name.
For ever and for ever and ever,
Hallowed be Thy Name.
Amen, Amen, it shall be so,
Hallowed be Thy Name.
Amen, Amen, it shall be so,
Hallowed be Thy Name.

West Indian Lord's Prayer

Words TRADITIONAL

Music TRADITIONAL
arr. Donald Swann

Hal-lowed be Thy Name. As we forgive those who tres-pass a-gainst us,
Hal-lowed be Thy Name. A - men, A - men, it shall be so, —

Dm   Gm7   C7   F   Am   B♭6   Dm   C7

1

Hal-lowed   be   Thy   Name.   And
Hal-lowed   be   Thy   Name.

ALL PERC.

F   C7   F   C7   C7   F

58

7
Message

I spent Christmas 1966 in the United States and there I received a Christmas card from the American Fellowship of Reconciliation. On it was a poem called *Message* and when I saw it was by a Vietnamese author I put it on the mantelpiece without reading it, certain I would only get distraught by being reminded of the tragedy of Vietnam, and that more worrying would help no one. One day however I picked it up and discovered that it was a message of love and sacrifice. I read it carefully and was deeply moved that the author, a poet and a monk, could be talking in peaceful words from that war-torn land. The poet is burying a dead comrade, and as he does so, he sees in the flowers and new grass around the grave the hope of new birth and new love. From that moment I thought: 'If this is Buddhism then I'm a Buddhist too.'

One day in 1971 there was a concert in London where Thich Nhat Hanh was present. I sang his song and thus met him for the first time. His moving book *The Lotus in the Sea of Fire* describes the yearning for peace by the ordinary Vietnamese and his poems do the same in passionate, anguished yet loving words. When peace comes to that country it will be as a result of the efforts of men like him.

Message

Life has left her footprints on my forehead
but I have become a child again this morning.
The smile, seen through leaves and flowers, is back, to smooth
away the wrinkles
As the rains wipe away footprints on the beach. Again a
cycle of birth and death begins.

I walk on thorns, but firmly, as among flowers.
I keep my head high.
Rhymes bloom among the sounds of bombs and mortars.
The tears I shed yesterday have become rain,
I feel calm hearing its sound on the thatched roof.
Childhood (o my birthland!) is calling me
And the rain melts my despair.

I am still here alive, able to smile quietly. The sweet fruit
brought forth by the tree of sufferings!
Carrying the dead body of my brother, I go across the rice-field
in the darkness.
Earth will keep thee tight within her arms, dear one,
so that to-morrow thou wilt be reincarnated in flowers—
those flowers smiling quietly in the morning field.
This moment you weep no more, dear one—we have gone through
too deep a night!

This morning, yes, this morning, I kneel down on the green grass
when I feel your presence.
O flowers which sing to me in silence!
The message
the message of love and sacrifice
has indeed come to us.

Message

Words by THICH NHAT HANH

Music by DONALD SWANN

Life has left_ her foot-prints on my fore-head but

I have be - come a child_____ a - gain this mor - ning.

The smile, seen_ through leaves and flowers,_ is
back, to smooth a-way_ the wrin-kles ____ As the
rains wipe a - way foot - prints on the beach.
A-gain a cy- cle of birth_ and death be -

sweet fruit__ brought forth by the tree of suf-fe-rings!

Car-ry-ing the dead bo-dy of my bro-ther, I

go a-cross the rice-field in the dark-ness.

Earth will keep thee tight with-in her

gone through too deep ____ a night!

This mor-ning, yes, ____ this mor-ning,   I

kneel down on the green grass when I feel your

68

Suggested pick for guitarist playing in E minor.
[if playing with piano use capo at 1st fret] :

8

Hail, Gladdening Light

As I became increasingly intrigued by new music and its reflections of new ideas, I was much assisted by a group of young people, the Swann Singers, who went from one church to another in a concert with me called *Soundings by Swann*. Our aim was to perform with the maximum clarity of diction, and with lightness of rhythm, so as to persuade our audiences that the new church could dispense with ponderousness, and that it could be gay and alerting. I wrote this evening hymn specially for these singers and dedicated it to them and to Herrick Bunney, the excellent organist and conductor of St Giles Cathedral, Edinburgh, who has so often brought such lightness of touch into his playing and choral conducting over twenty-five years at the Cathedral.

Of all the things I would like to do with carols, it is this; to lighten the strain that too many people have felt about faith, God, religion and Christianity. Too many people have been weighed down by it all instead of encouraged. Maybe that era is now over. The musical *Godspell* has tried to lighten things; Jesus is a dancer in Sydney Carter's famous *Lord of the Dance* song; the new Jesus who is festive and laughing has come to meet us often in the last ten years. Long may he stay. The sorrowing Jesus will stay too, but Jesus is both of these moods and many more.

The words of *Hail, Gladdening Light* are fourth-century Greek, translated by John Keble into nineteenth-century English and here is a twentieth-century tune of mine. Is this the one world of carols? I hope so.

Hail, Gladdening Light

Hail, glad'ning light, of his pure glory pour'd,
Who is the immortal Father, heav'nly blest,
Holiest of holies, Jesus Christ, our Lord.
Now we are come to the sun's hour of rest,
The lights of evening round us shine,
We hymn the Father, Son and Holy Spirit divine.
Worthiest art Thou at all times to be sung
With undivided tongue.
Son of our God, Giver of life alone:
Therefore in all the world
Thy glories, Lord, they own.

Hail, Gladdening Light

Words : 4th century Greek
translated by JOHN KEBLE

Music by DONALD SWANN

✱ *The Double Bass should play the lowest notes of the piano bass part; the Guitar should always follow the rhythm of the right hand of the piano.*
When both these instruments are used the piano may (and preferably should) be omitted.

76

In all the world Thy glo - ries, Lord,— they own.
(they)

9

Pilgrims' Hymn

I once spent a month with my family in a little town outside Jerusalem called Ramallah where we stayed in the Friends' Boys School, as a guest of the Headmaster. I had first seen the school in 1944 in Palestine under the British Mandate, and the month I am referring to now was twenty-one years later in 1965. I have just been there again and thus seen it with three rulers: under the British, in Arab Jordan, and as a town in the Israeli-occupied West Bank. It was in this town I felt more strongly than anywhere else that the centres of power on this earth, religious or political, are but shadows, and it is the people who are real. The prophets of all the religions are their leaders calling them to live by the spirit: there was only ever one world, it did not take television or aeroplanes to unite it, it existed from the first, and the people of the spirit are its inhabitants and no barrier has ever divided them: there is only one battle, and that is for courtesy to one's neighbour, and for solace for him when he is in trouble, and this is the only battle worth fighting. However these people of the spirit are too often being forced into over-strict mental and political patterns: but they are brave and become pilgrims, living but lightly bound to the ties they resent.

In Ramallah, all this came out in a *Pilgrims' Hymn*. I wrote the line about the flag unfurled without thinking of any flag in mind, but when I got to New York I saw it on sale in an exhibition aptly called 'The People Yes'; the flag of the earth, a fine blue flag showing the earth as seen from the moon, the creation of artist Norman Laliberté and of John McConnell, a remarkable pioneering American who hopes to get us all a new public holiday, 'The Whole Earth Day'!

The Rev. Philip Eastman of *Reconciliation* magazine set the song into orbit, as he first printed and issued it in one issue as a special handout.

Pilgrims' Hymn

We ask that we live and we labour in peace, in peace
Each man shall be our neighbour in peace, in peace
Distrust and hatred will turn to love,
All the prisoners freed,
And our only war will be the one
Against all human need.

We work for the end of disunion in truth, in truth
That all may be one communion in truth, in truth
We choose the road of peace and prayer
Countless pilgrims trod,
So that Hindu, Moslem, Christian, Jew
We all can worship one God.

We call to our friends and our brothers, unite, unite!
That all may live for others, unite, unite!
And so the nations will be as one,
One the flag unfurled,
One law, one faith, one hope, one truth,
One people and one world.

Pilgrims' Hymn

Words and Music by
DONALD SWANN

10

The Wassail of Figgy Duff

The Babe is born in Bethlehem,
The Angel Choirs sing.
The Magi and the Shepherds hear
Glad tidings of their King.
The Mother smiles, the star shines on,
The heavens can relax,
And Joseph wonders how on earth
He's going to pay his tax.

Michael Flanders, who wrote the above, is not alone in having a rather down-to-earth view of Christmas, nor in deploring its more commercial aspects on the lines of:

In the bleak mid-winter
Santa's at the store.
Have you sent a greeting
To the dog next door?

There are moments in the festive season when we're inclined to be grateful that

Christmas comes but once a year,
When it's gone we raise a cheer.

Even in a Christmas carol service the occasional pagan note can be refreshing. Michael Flanders and I (really he—I was the enabler at the piano) parodied the kind of old English Wassail Song, which is so 'lay', it conveys no Christian message whatsoever, in this carol called *The Wassail of Figgy Duff*.

The Wassail of Figgy Duff

Oh Christmasse is icum
Mark ye Robin's ruddy tum
And ye winde it-te bloweth very rough—
Rough—rough,
Now do as ye be tolde
To keepe us from ye colde
And fille us up with Figgy, Figgy Duff,
Figgy Duff.

So merrily we sing
For to make ye Welkin ring
Though of singing we have had-de quite enough—
Nough—nough,
My maisters if you please
Give us a mouldy cheese
To eat with our Figgy, Figgy Duff,
Figgy Duff.

If a cheese ye have not got
Then a groat must be our lot
As we dance round the Mistletoe Buff—
(Bough)—Buff!
* If you haven't got a groat
You can go and cut your throat
And ne'er have any Figgy, Figgy
Ne'er have any Figgy, Figgy
Ne'er have any Figgy, Figgy Duff,
Figgy Duff.

* *Cecil Sharp gives variant (Yorkshire, West Riding and Scunthorpe)*
  If you've nothing on your shelfe
  You can go and hang yourselfe
Cf. Revised Version (Donald Swann: 'A Child's Garland of Carols')
  If you've naught would feed a mouse,
  Happy Christmas! Bless this house!

The Wassail of Figgy Duff

Traditional Words and Music
invented by MICHAEL FLANDERS

Fairly fast, but with pauses for 'effect'

Lyrics under the staves:

Oh

Christ-masse is i - cum Mark ye Rob-in's rud-dy tum And ye winde it - te blow-eth ve - ry

rough - rough - rough, Now do as ye be tolde To keepe us from ye colde And

* Each time this 'echo' may be 8va alt. or 8va basso or even 16va alt. or 16va basso if you have
   such prodigies in your choir!

I I

Red and Green Christmas

At Christmas time for the last four or five years I have always played the song *Red and Green Christmas* somewhere to someone. It is by Nadia Cattouse, the folk singer and composer from British Honduras, who has now made England her home. I enjoy accompanying her wonderful warm voice, but when she is not there I perform the song with my own singers or alone with my unwonderful cool voice trying to lilt the tune while embroidering the key-board with arpeggios.

Nadia's tune captures the nostalgia that every person from a warm climate must feel as they sit next to an electric fire and wish that the mistletoe were hibiscus and the holly were honeypalm—and that leads me to poinsettia! Nadia was sure it was 'poinsietta', with the stress on the first syllable. A long sojourn in England close to the *Concise Oxford Dictionary* has proved to her that the word is poinsettia. But it's too late; the tune insists on the first pronounciation, so 'poinsietta' has to stay. Long live the variations of English spoken all over the world!

Nadia herself says: 'On a sparkling white wintry walk between Woburn and Milton Bryan vicarage one Christmas some years ago, the words of this song first began to float into my mind. Although written at Christmas, the song really belongs to all the months of the year. For now, it represents the colour, the warmth, the simplicity, the whole happy adventure of my early life in British Honduras.'

Red and Green Christmas

Mine was a red and green Christmas,
A scarlet poinsietta Christmas,
A seagreen honeypalm Christmas,
Ah mine was a red and green Christmas.

Mine was a red and green Christmas,
A scented frangipane Christmas,
A leafy oleander Christmas,
Ah mine was a red and green Christmas.

Every door and window wide,
Sound of music everywhere.
Church bells ringing peace on earth
And good will for all to share.

Mine was a red and green Christmas,
A flaming poinciana Christmas,
A warm hibiscus Christmas,
Ah mine was a red and green Christmas.

Red and Green Christmas

Words and Music by
NADIA CATTOUSE

This is an arrangement for solo voice, with other backing voices. However, a solo singer could readily use it, as it is basically a simple 32-bar melody with a coda.

The arpeggios in the right hand are very much part of my style and are not too difficult, as the piece moves in an easy tempo. Even the two bars of "23's" are but a straight cascade of descending thirds marked 'meno mosso' and can thus be done in the pianist's best tempo. However, if this is too hard altogether omit the right hand at these points and just support the voices with the left: the song won't be spoiled.

© *1973 by Galliard Ltd.*

91

93

94

For simple, shortened version
go on to coda.

95

Christmas, Ah mine _____ was a red and green Christ - mas.

Ev - ery door and win-dow wide, _ Sound of mu - sic ev - ery-where._

Church bells ring-ing peace on earth _ And good will for _

molto accel.

cresc.

più mosso e animato

più mosso

f

f

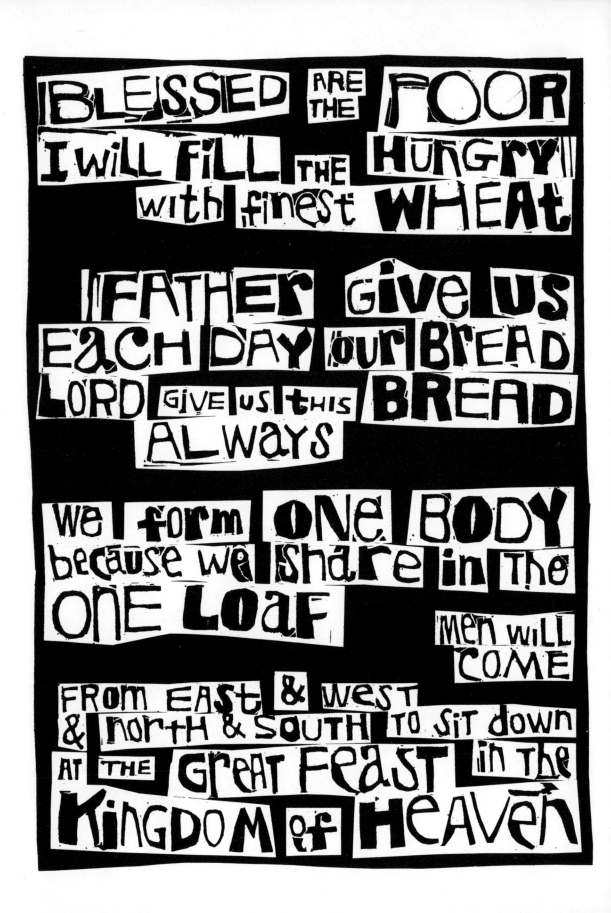

12

I Want to go Out

The wonderful list of songs of praise that we have inherited appear never to include indecision. Or if they do, I've missed them. 'We praise thee, we bless thee', they say. It takes a twentieth-century writer to say openly, 'I bless him, but sometimes I don't bless him; I want to be welcomed and also I want to keep clear.' Perhaps all this is another way of saying that now we seek an element of *drama* in our songs, even in our songs of praise; and that we acknowledge the psychological inability of many of us to hold an idea or a faith steadily between the sights for any length of time.

David Goodall who wrote the words and the tune of *I Want to go Out* is a Congregationalist minister and wrote this song for a Scottish hymn book called *Dunblane Praises*. I have found it exciting to perform solo with the words repeated at speed by the congregation, so that is how I have written it out in the music, but of course this repetition is not obligatory. If you *are* trying my way, consider using the piano behind the first line and then organ behind the second line.

I Want to go Out

I want to go out,
I want to go home,
I want to be single,
I want to belong,
I want to grow up,
I want to stay young,
I want to do both and all at once and anything else that takes my fancy whether
    it hurts or helps to pass the time of day:
Show me the way!

Now tell me a tale,
Or say me a prayer,
Bring on the preacher,
And let him declare,
'We're going to heaven,
For heaven's up there.'
But what of the folks who stay below and live and die and never recollect the
    tales they heard in their forgotten youth?
Tell them the truth!

One Saturday night
I sat all alone,
And when it was Sunday
Went out on my own.
I came to the church,
They opened the door.
But when I got in the congregation looked the same as me and everyone as
    lonely as a man without a wife,
Looking for life.

I want to go out,
I want to stay here,
I want to be welcomed,
I want to keep clear;
I want to believe,
I want to be sure.
Show me the man who knows the way, the truth, the life and who is yesterday,
    today and everlastingly the same;
Tell me his name!

I Want to go Out

Words and Music by
DAVID GOODALL

© 1973 D. P. S. Publicity Ltd.
Reprinted by permission

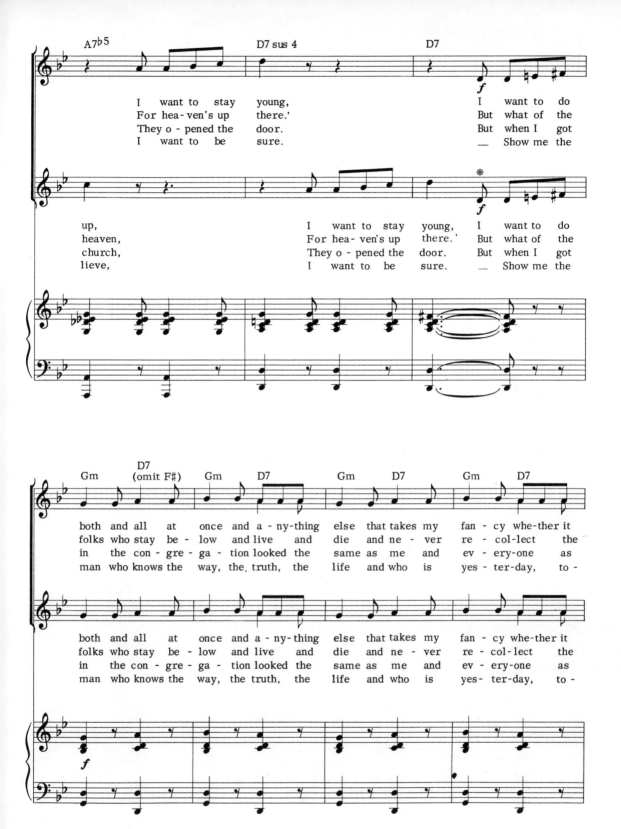

* If Voice I is a solo, I suggest let him or her take this long line alone; i. e. Voice II becomés tacet here for 8 bars.

13

St Nicholas

Greece is a perpetual source of inspiration to me after three exciting years among Greeks at the end of the war—in the Middle East, the Dodecanese Islands and in mainland Epirus. I used to listen enraptured to the Greek folk music and on my return to this colder country in 1948 to complete an Oxford course in modern Greek, I thought I had heard all the Greek musical rhythms. I was wrong. I heard some thrilling new ones in Herne Hill in South London from the Cypriot composer and bouzouki player Andreas Toumazis, whose wife incidentally makes a magnificent grape sausage, a Cypriot delicacy.

Andreas's tune is in $\frac{9}{8}$ but stressed as 2–2–2–3. This rhythm is not as formidable to learn as it looks and my daughter soon chose it from these many songs to pick out at the piano. I have written into the 'barbaric' tune the dramatic miracle story of St Nicholas who was Middle Eastern like Andreas.

St Nicholas

Once there was great
Famine and dearth;
People were starved,
Bare was the earth.
Three boys were caught,
Cut up for meat,
Salted and served
Ready to eat.
St Nicholas,
Great was his soul,
Bade them stand forth,
Made them all whole.

Now when we see
Children in war,
Their bodies burned,
Broken and sore,
What can we do?
What can we say?
To you, St Ni-
Cholas, we pray:
St Nicholas,
Rid them of pain,
Bring them alive
For us again.

St Nicholas

Words by
DONALD SWANN

Music by
ANDREAS TOUMAZIS

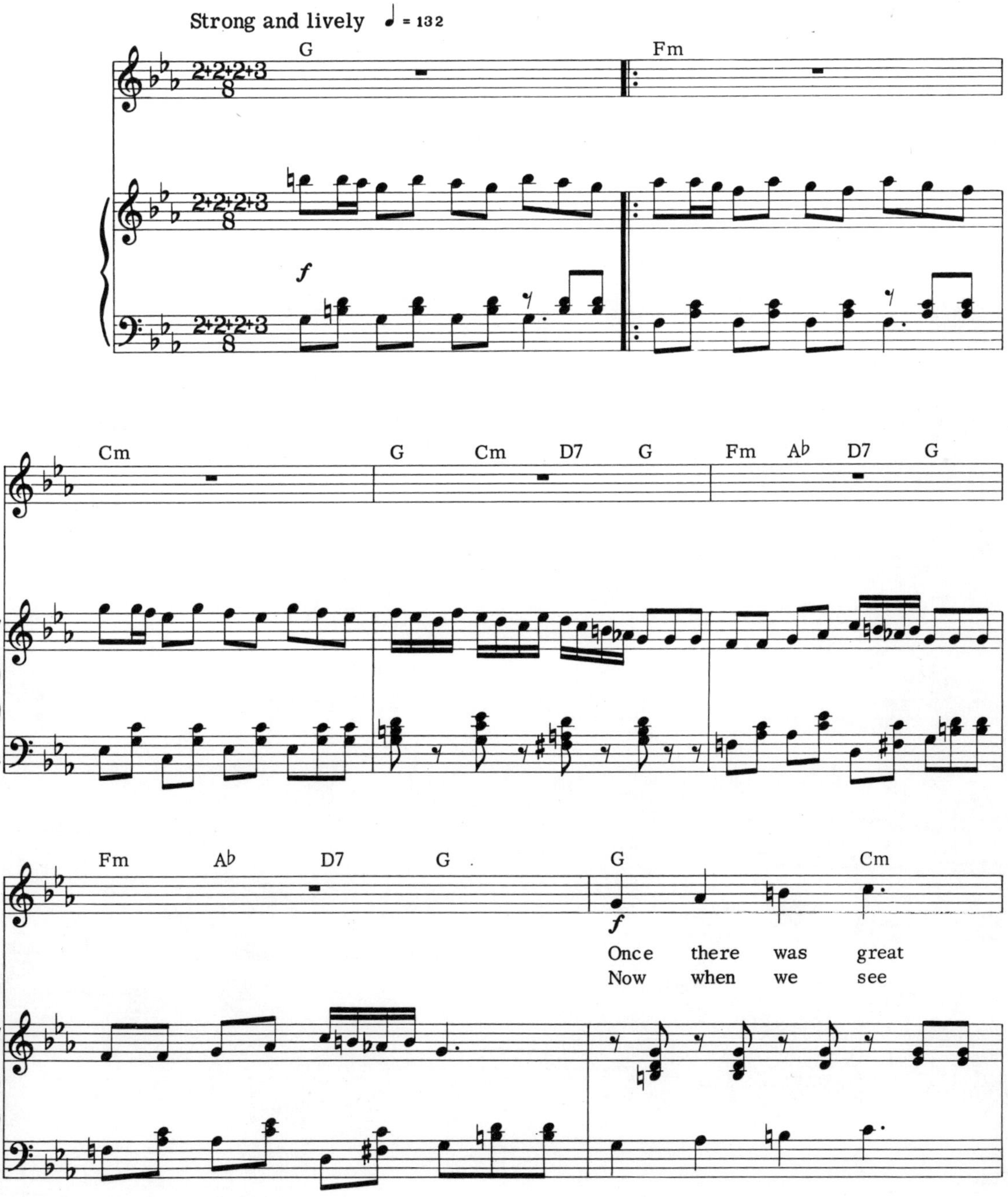

Strong and lively ♩ = 132
G
Fm
Cm
G Cm D7 G
Fm A♭ D7 G
Fm A♭ D7 G
G Cm
f
Once there was great
Now when we see

Fm6 Cm G7(sus 4) Cm G Cm

Fa - mine and dearth; Peo - ple were starved,
Chil - dren in war, Their bod - ies burned,

Fm Ab G7 Cm G Ab G7 Cm

Bare was the earth.
Bro - ken and sore,

Abdim G7 Cm Cm

Three boys were caught,
(V.2-**p**) What can we do?

Fm6 Bdim Fm D7b5 Abdim G7

Cut _ up _ for _ meat, Sal - ted and served Rea - dy _ to _ eat. _
What _ can _ we _ say? To you Saint Ni - Cho - las, _ we pray: _

St Ni - cho - las, Great was his soul,
(V.2 f) St Ni - cho - las, Rid them of pain,

Bade them stand forth, Made them all whole.
Bring them a - live For us a - gain.

14

Too Much to Do

In June 1970 I played a concert of Cretan songs in Nicosia with the soprano, Lilli Malandraki, and a composer came round afterwards and introduced himself as Achilleas Lymbourides. He said he wrote songs in similar vein to the ones we were performing and could we come and hear some of them at his flat. It turned out that Lymbourides is to Cyprus roughly what Hadjithakis is to Greece; he has captured the folk idiom of Cyprus and made it his own in original words and lyrics. He played to us on record and on his unaccompanied violin a whole clutch of excellent melodies, but trust my half-Slavonic soul (I am over half-Russian) the one I fell for was dreamy and melodic and as different from Andreas Toumazis' *St Nicholas* with its rugged $\frac{9}{8}$ as you could have it.

This gave me the idea for my own lyric; a man wakes in the night and hears a voice exhorting him 'Wake up and take action about the world's problems.' He turns over and returns to his dream of utopia. A cynical carol? No, a little irony only.

Too Much to Do

Last night I suddenly woke, and knew I'd been dreaming
That the wildest hopes of man had all come true.
And all the earth was peaceful, the sky was clear and blue,
The ages of war and hunger and pain were through.

I lay awake, and then I turned on the radio
And I heard a voice cry out—I don't know who—
'Awake, awake my brothers, awake my sisters too,
There's so much for us, there's so much for us to do.'

I listened to him; he spoiled the mood of my dreaming,
And I feared it might be me that he was talking to.
So I went back to dreaming, to that dream that would never
    come true;
There's far too much, too much for me to do.

Too Much to Do

Words by
DONALD SWANN

Music by
ACHILLEAS LYMBOURIDES

* *Low for Sopranos and Tenors, but let them try. After all, it's very quiet.*

15

Don't Wait for an Angel

When I realised that so many carols in this book were from 'abroad' I began to get a bit jealous for England, which is my home. What of the hundreds of new songs being written here, emerging either under the paper covers of Galliard, or from religious folk groups on the move between churches, in break-through services in Liverpool Cathedral, in Michael Lehr's 'Reflection' evenings designed to introduce congregations to new musical material, in Barry Wilsher's 'Rejoicings' concerts of music and drama, or in pioneering school assemblies? There is no limit at all to the experimentation in this country but there still remain people altogether untouched by these flowing rivers of innovation. How do they escape? Perhaps because their ideas are set for all time and nothing but an earthquake will move them.

The Reverend Caryl Micklem, a bold pioneer in this field, wrote this next carol, both the words and the music, for the magazine *New Christian* at Christmas 1968, putting his excellent journalistic skill this time into a song. He is impatient. 'Don't wait for an angel,' he says, 'get up and finish the work that was started on Christmas Day.' I greatly admire this attacking spirit.

Don't Wait for an Angel

Don't wait for an angel,
Don't look for a star,
To tell you the message
Or guide you from far.
These are part of the background
For art-lovers' eyes,
To help them to measure
The portrait for size.

    He's only a baby
    To grow to a man:
    To call you to finish
    The work he began.

It isn't to Bethlehem
Shepherds must go,
But to look for the missing lamb
Under the snow.
It isn't on camels
That real kings ride,
But on asses and crosses
With robbers beside.

    He's only a baby
    To grow to a man:
    To call you to finish
    The work he began.

Now all you good people
From bench and from sink,
Come turn up the volume
And hear yourselves think:
Who else on his birthday's
Put back in a cot?
Do you reckon Act One
Is as good as the lot?

    He's only a baby
    To grow to a man:
    To call you to finish
    The work he began.

Don't Wait for an Angel

Words and Music by
CARYL MICKLEM

Briskly (in One)

Don't wait for an an - gel, Don't look for a star, To
It is - n't to Beth - le - hem Shep - herds must go, But to
Now all you good peo - ple From bench and from sink, Come

tell you the mes - sage Or guide you from far. These are
look for the mis - sing lamb Un - der the snow. It
turn up the vol - ume And hear your - selves think: Who

part of the back-ground For art-lov-ers' eyes, To
is - n't on cam - els That re - al kings ride, But on
else on his birth-day's Put back in a cot? Do you

help them to mea-sure The por - trait for size. He's
ass - es and cross - es With rob-bers be - side. He's
rec-kon Act One Is as good as the lot? He's

on - ly a ba - by To grow to a man: To_ call you to
on - ly a ba - by To grow to a man: To_ call you to
on - ly a ba - by To grow to a man: To_ call you to

1-2
fin-ish The work he be - gan.
fin-ish The work he be - gan.
fin-ish The

3 *poco rit.*
work he be - gan.

poco rit.

128

16
No Man May Shorten the Way

This song finds its way into the book from my opera *Perelandra* where it occurs at the climax of the adventure.

I worked on this opera for several years together with David Marsh, who contributed two lyrics to my first carol collection *Sing Round the Year*. The story of the opera is based on the late Dr C. S. Lewis's novel *Perelandra* and is about a beautiful planet that nearly falls into the hands of evil forces, but is rescued in the nick of time. This short synopsis makes it sound like a science fiction cliché, but it has the excitement of *Paradise Lost* without the obscure references. *No Man May Shorten the Way* has often been performed outside the context of the opera, so I felt justified in including it here. It is for a solo, or for unison choir, and it makes some demands on the voice in plainsong style. I have found it effective to include it in programmes as a challenging contrast to the lighter pieces, and it answers the accusation made by some, that many new carols are too superficial. Furthermore singers with trained voices do not get enough to do when the 'folk material' gets going, and that doesn't suit me because I greatly admire a well-trained voice and especially one that can hold pitch when partly unaccompanied, as required here.

No Man May Shorten the Way

No man may shorten the way.
Each must carry his cross
On the long road to Calvary,
Follow
Where other feet have trodden.
Though the burden seems too great
For bleeding shoulders to uphold,
Too dark the path
For failing eyes to see,
Yet the lonely hill must still be climbed,
The desolation still be borne.
No man may shorten the way.

No Man May Shorten the Way

Words by
DAVID MARSH

Music by
DONALD SWANN

Gently ♩ = 84

No man may shor-ten the way.＿ Each must car-ry his

cross＿ On the long road, on the long road to Cal - va - ry,

Fol - low, fol - - - low,＿ fol - - - - low,

fol - - - - - - low,__ fol - - low where o-ther__ feet have

trod-den. Though the bur-den seems too great For blee - - - - ding

shoul-ders__to up - hold, Too dark the path For fai - ling eyes__ to __

see,__ Yet the lone - - - ly hill__ must still be

climbed, The des - - - - o - - la - - - tion
still __ be borne. No man may shor-ten the way. __

Each must car-ry his cross __ On the long _____ road, on the

long _____ road to Cal - - - - va - ry. __

ONE MORE STEP ALONG
TRAVELING
KEEP ME
of the
the
corners
WORLD
ALONG
i turn
WORLD
MORE & MORE
ABOUT the
i GO
WORLD,
WITH YOU
I
to the new
Round the
Learn
from
TRAVEL!
the OLD

17

One More Step

A year ago Sydney Carter was asked by the Reverend Roger Royle, of Southwark Cathedral, to write a song appropriate for young children to sing together at a service or assembly held before they move to a higher school—an end-of-school hymn. But it did not take long for his friends to see that here was a carol for any one of us moving from anywhere to anywhere! Furthermore it makes a perfect New Year carol, 'And it's from the old I travel to the new.' *One More Step* is another of Sydney Carter's 'moving' carols; in his songs everyone is always travelling or dancing, or flying like a bird of heaven. The melody of this song has overtones of the Salvation Army (I can see them in the street, moving from corner to corner) and of the Mission songs I heard as a little boy at the seaside (more outdoor movement). Of all the songs I have ever taught audiences this is the easiest for them to pick up.

I have wondered, in spite of my admiration for Sydney, where is the doctrine of unalterability, and fastness? God used to be a safe stronghold, a big tower. Now according to Sydney he is always travelling. Are these new hymns the hymns of the world in mobility, where even sculptures (that used to be rock-firm) are mobile? Or have we discovered that God as a Holy Spirit is always moving, and that other ages tried to fix him in error?

One More Step

One more step along the world I go,
One more step along the world I go.
From the old things to the new
Keep me travelling along with you.
    And it's from the old I travel to the new
    Keep me travelling along with you.

Round the corners of the world I turn,
More and more about the world I learn.
All the new things that I see
You'll be looking at along with me.
    And it's from the old I travel to the new
    Keep me travelling along with you.

As I travel through the bad and good
Keep me travelling the way I should.
Where I see no way to go
You'll be telling me the way, I know.
    And it's from the old I travel to the new
    Keep me travelling along with you.

Keep me singing when the road is rough
Give me courage when the world is tough.
Leap and laugh in all I do,
Keep me travelling along with you.
    And it's from the old I travel to the new
    Keep me travelling along with you.

You are older than the world can be.
You are younger than the life in me.
Ever old and ever new,
Keep me travelling along with you.
    And it's from the old I travel to the new
    Keep me travelling along with you.

One More Step

Words and Music by
SYDNEY CARTER

One more step a - long the world I go,
Round the cor - ners of the world I turn,
As I tra - vel through the bad and good
Keep me sing - ing when the road is rough,
You are ol - der than the world can be.

One more step a - long the world I go.
More and more a - bout the world I learn.
Keep me tra - vel - ling the way I should.
Give me cou - rage when the world is tough.
You are youn - ger than the life in me.

From the old things to the new   Keep me tra - vel-ling a -
All the new things that I see   You'll be look- ing at a -
Where I see no way to go   You'll be tel - ling me the
Leap and laugh in all I do,   Keep me tra - vel-ling a -
Ev - er old and ev - er new,   Keep me tra - vel-ling a -

long with you.
long with me.
way, I know. And it's from   the old I
long with you.
long with you.

tra-vel to the new   Keep me tra - vel-ling a - long with you.

138

18
Christmas Candle

I never thought I would come out strongly emotional about 'a song my mother taught me', but here it is Лучинушка a Russian folk song to which I have written my own words. My mother was a Moslem and came from Caucasus; she was a folk singer, mainly of Russian gypsy songs and of popular Russian melodies like this one.

Christmas Candle, with my newly written words, was first performed when a group of beautiful Swedish girls sang it in a television programme devised by Helen Best concerning the Swedish Festival of Lights. Incidentally enhancing the international mixture still further, they also sang the Italian song *Santa Lucia*, traditionally sung at this Festival in Sweden.

The musical arrangement of *Christmas Candle* for this book is for four parts *à la russe*. As for the title and subject, I have always loved candles and indeed I *have* burned them all night to cheer up my insomnia. The best candle smell ever was in Mount Athos at Easter Eve Service; because the service lasted all night, the smell increased in intensity through the hours.

Christmas Candle

All night long I shall burn my Christmas candle,
Watch the flame burning yellow, grey and blue.
Pierce my eyes, my shining Christmas candle,
Oh clear my eyes so that I can see anew.
Pierce my eyes, my shining Christmas candle,
Oh shine your light so that I can see anew.

All night long I shall burn my Christmas candle,
I shall watch till the wax has all burned through.
Burn my heart, my shining Christmas candle,
Oh shine your light so my heart can burn anew.
Oh come and burn my heart, my shining Christmas candle,
Oh touch my heart so that I can feel anew.

Christmas Candle

Words by DONALD SWANN

Music: RUSSIAN TRADITIONAL
arr. Donald Swann

shi-ning Christ-mas can - dle, Oh shine your light so my eyes can see a - new.

shi-ning Christmas can - dle, Oh shine your light so my eyes can see a - new.

All night long I shall burn my Christ-mas can - dle, I shall

All night long I shall watch till the wax has all burned through.

burn my Christ-mas can - dle, I shall watch till the wax has all burned through.

Burn my heart, Burn_ my heart,_ my shi-ning Christ-mas can - dle, Oh

Burn_ my heart, my shi-ning Christ-mas can - dle, Oh

19
Half the World

In November 1971 I was about to go on a tour of the Middle East and felt I wanted to find the song which best summed up, out of all the many that had been written, the division of the world into haves and have-nots. In my opinion this song *Half the World*—music by John Scott, words by Joan Maitland—is the one. 'Which side are you on, brother? Think before the night.' As we sang this in Cairo and Amman, I asked myself on which side was I? At least I had raised the question, I consoled myself.

With my singers we divide the lines so that a new voice takes up the challenge. John Scott, as well as being a composer, is an excellent arranger and for a record by Nadia Cattouse he made an instrumental arrangement of my song, *Message*. I've tried to repay the compliment with my piano version of his song.

Half the World

Half the world is starving,
Half the world is over-fed;
Half take sleeping pills at night,
Half don't have a bed.
Half is struggling to live,
Half is sitting tight;
Which side are you on, brother?
Think before the night.

Half the world is seeing,
Half the world is blind;
Half the world's intolerant,
Half the world is kind.
Half just want their children fed,
Half don't heed their plight;
Which side are you on, brother?
Think before the night.

Half the world is crooked,
Half the world is straight;
Half the world has loving hearts,
Half is full of hate.
Half would kill his fellow man,
Half don't want to fight;
Which side are you on, brother?
Think before the night.

Never mind your country,
Never mind your skin;
Never mind which God you love,
Which half you're in.
Half is struggling to live,
Half is sitting tight;
Which side are you on, brother?
Think before the night.
Think hard, brother,
Think before the night.

Half the World

Words and Music by
JOAN MAITLAND
and JOHN SCOTT

Strong and forceful ♩. = 58

Guitar: full single chords, *sf* , each time and let ring.

Half the	world	is	star-ving,	Half the
Half the	world	is	see-ing,	Half the
Half the	world	is	croo-ked,	Half the
Ne-ver	mind	your	coun-try,	Ne-ver

world   is o - ver - fed;   Half   take
world   is   blind;   Half   the
world   is   straight;   Half   the
mind   your   skin;   Ne - ver

slee-ping pills   at   night,   Half   don't   have _____ a
world's   in - tol - er - ant,   Half   the   world _____ is
world   has lov - ing hearts,   Half   is   full _____ of
mind   which God you love,   Which half _____ you're

bed.   Half   is   strugg - ling to
kind.   Half   just want their chil - dren
hate.   Half   would kill his fel - low
in.   Half   is   strugg - ling to

live,   Half   is   sit - ting   tight; ___
fed,   Half   don't heed their plight; ___
man,   Half   don't want to   fight; ___
live,   Half   is   sit - ting   tight; ___

Which side are you on, bro-ther?_

Think be-fore the night.

CODA after last verse

Think hard, bro-ther,_ Think be - fore the

night.

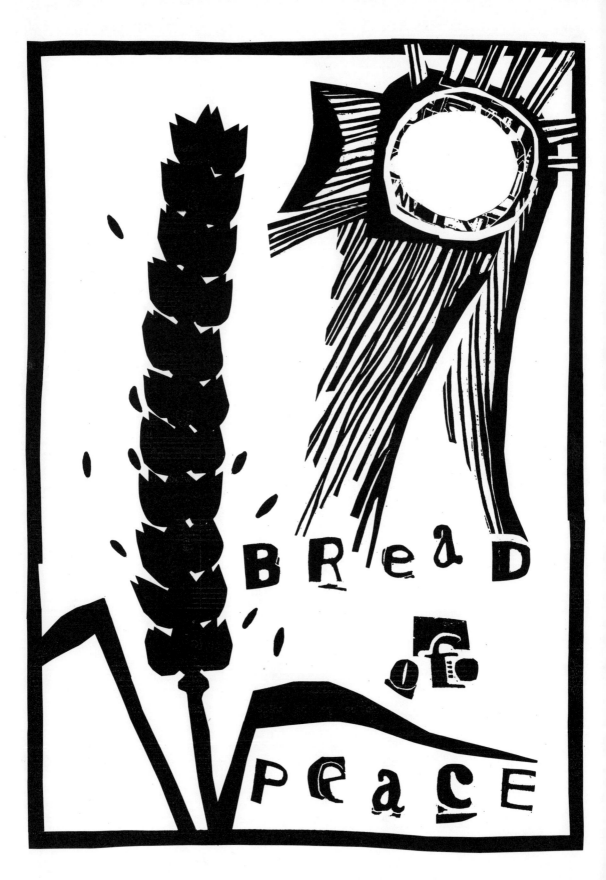

20

Make us Worthy, Lord

Mother Teresa's daily prayer

I spent much time seeking a final song for this book, feeling strongly
that I needed a peaceful one after the challenge of *Half the World*. The
pattern I sought in my mind is used by Michel Quoist in one of his
Prayers of Life. 'Lord, why did you tell me to love all men, my brothers?'
I have in fact set this prayer to music, but could not include it here as
the publishers rightly complained it was fiendishly difficult both to
sing and to play. Quoist asks a terrifying question. How can we respond
to all the claims on us? There are so many unhappy needy people and
we keep meeting more. God replies, 'When all men came into you,
I came among them.' I wanted that sort of answer to *Half the World*.
It came when I was introduced to Mother Teresa's daily prayer. My
group of singers and I were doing a concert connected with co-
workers of Mother Teresa, and the Reverend John Hambidge in
charge of the event, himself a co-worker, said, 'Why not set the
prayer on the front of the programme?'

A few months later when I'd written the music, Mother Teresa
wrote, 'You may by all means use it as a song to lift people's minds to
the love of God, and of Him in His distressing disguise, the Poor.'

Mother Teresa's love and care for the poor, suffering and dying,
answers the challenge of *Half the World*, and her daily prayer provides
me with the peaceful last song I sought. I thank her.

Make us Worthy, Lord

Mother Teresa's daily prayer

Make us worthy, Lord,
To serve our fellow men
Throughout the world who live and die
In poverty and hunger.

Give them, through our hands,
This day, their daily bread,
And by our understanding Love,
Give Peace and Joy.

Make us Worthy, Lord

Mother Teresa's daily prayer

Words
TRADITIONAL

Music by
DONALD SWANN

Words used by permission.
Music © 1973 by Galliard Ltd.

❋ I've found it quite possible for an audience to pick up the 'mirror' second line at first hearing,
especially if the words are in their hands. If attempting this (minus a choir) omit the choral obbligato
between verses.

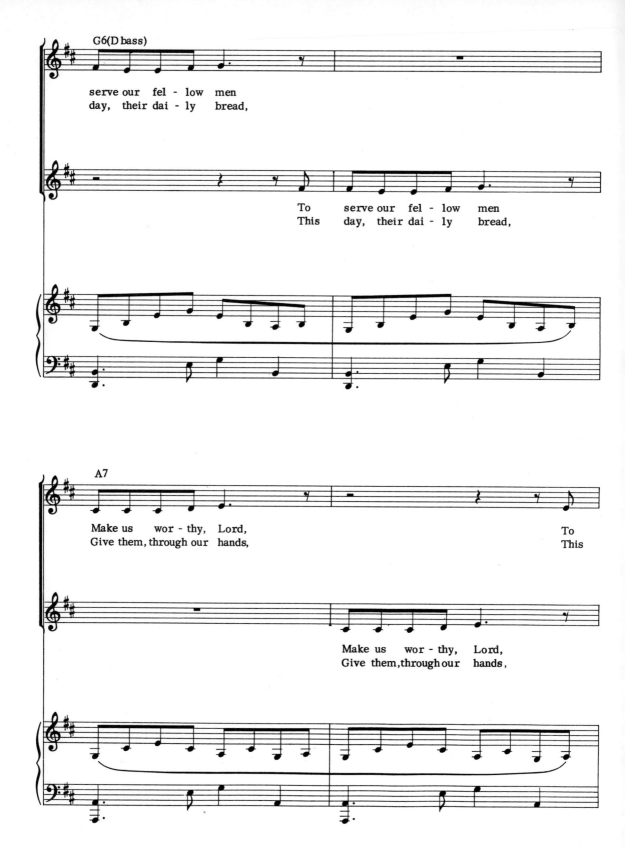

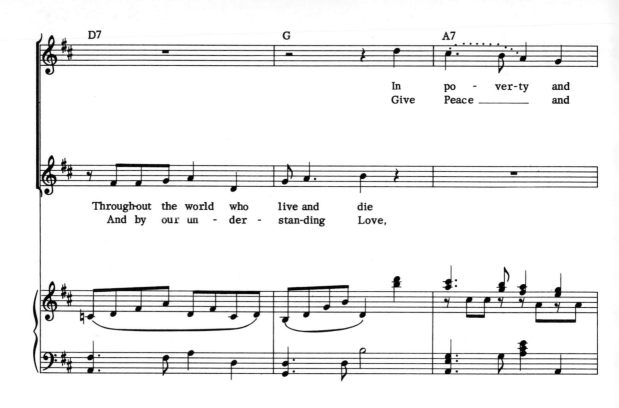

In po - ver-ty and
Give Peace _____ and

Throughout the world who live and die
And by our un - der - stan-ding Love,

hun-ger. _____
Joy. _____

In po - ver-ty and hun-ger. _____
Give Peace _____ and Joy. _____

In
Give

158

po- ver - ty and hun - - - ger.
Peace _____ and Joy.

ALL VOICES

Ah _____

Ah _____

la la la la la   la   la _____